Little BRAINIACS PRESCHOOL ™

COUNTING FUN

Count the pictures in each group.
Circle the correct number.

2   7   5

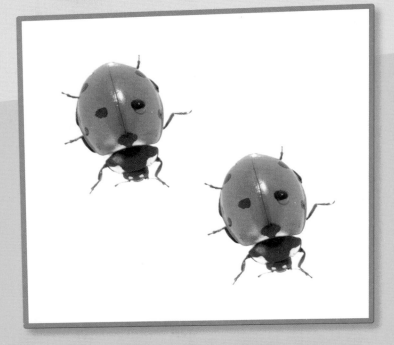

8   4   7

6   1   3

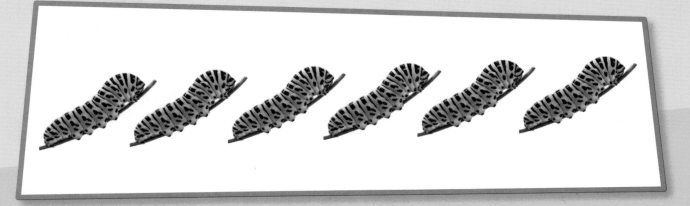

ANSWERS

COUNTING FUN

Count the pictures in each group.
Circle the correct number.

(2)　7　5

8　(4)　7

(6)　1　3

GROCERY STORE MAZE

Return the shopping cart to the grocery store by following the maze.

Store

ANSWERS

GROCERY STORE MAZE

Return the shopping cart to the grocery store by following the maze.

Store

LET'S FIND ANIMALS
IN THE NEIGHBORHOOD

Look at the pictures.
Circle **6** animals you might
find in a neighborhood.

ANSWERS

LET'S FIND ANIMALS IN THE NEIGHBORHOOD

Look at the pictures. Circle **6** animals you might find in a neighborhood.

This or That?

Draw a circle around the animals that are found in the ocean.

 **or**

fish   zebra

 **or**

llama   lobster

 **or**

shark   rabbit

 **or**

crab   raccoon

ANSWERS

This or That?

Draw a circle around the animals that are found in the ocean.

fish or zebra

llama or lobster

shark or rabbit

crab or raccoon

THE BIGGEST!

Circle the picture in each row that is biggest.

ANSWERS

THE BIGGEST!

Circle the picture in each row that is biggest.

The smallest!

Circle the picture in each group that is the smallest.

43

ANSWERS

The smallest!

Circle the picture in each group that is the smallest.

Search & Find®
IN THE RAIN FOREST

Search & Find® the pictures of the animals in the rain forest.
Circle each animal as you find it.

fish

butterfly

toucan

iguana

jaguar

ANSWERS

Search & Find® IN THE RAIN FOREST

Search & Find® the pictures of the animals in the rain forest.
Circle each animal as you find it.

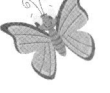

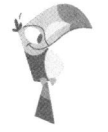

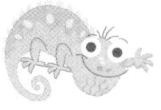

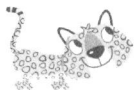

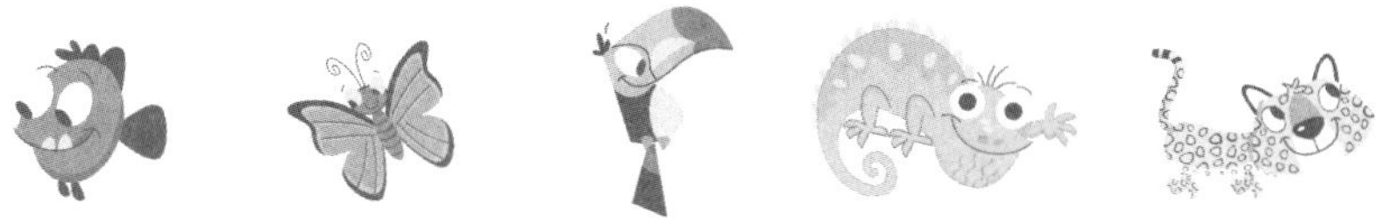

fish | butterfly | toucan | iguana | jaguar

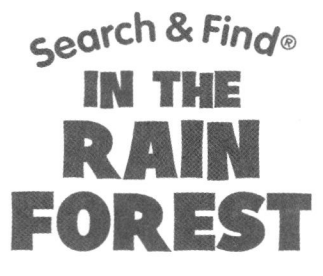

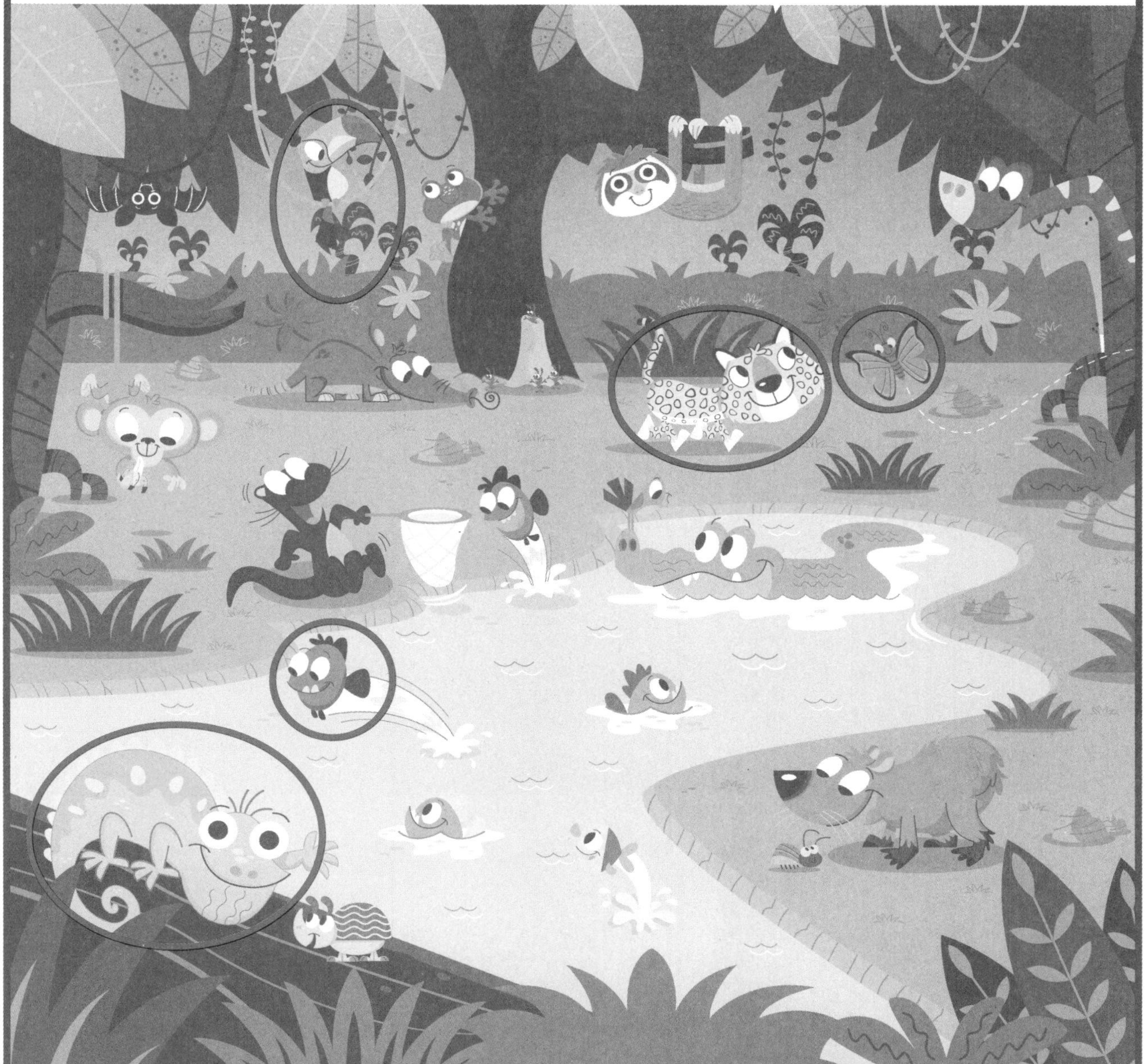

LET'S FIND RHYMES!

Draw a line to connect the rhymes.

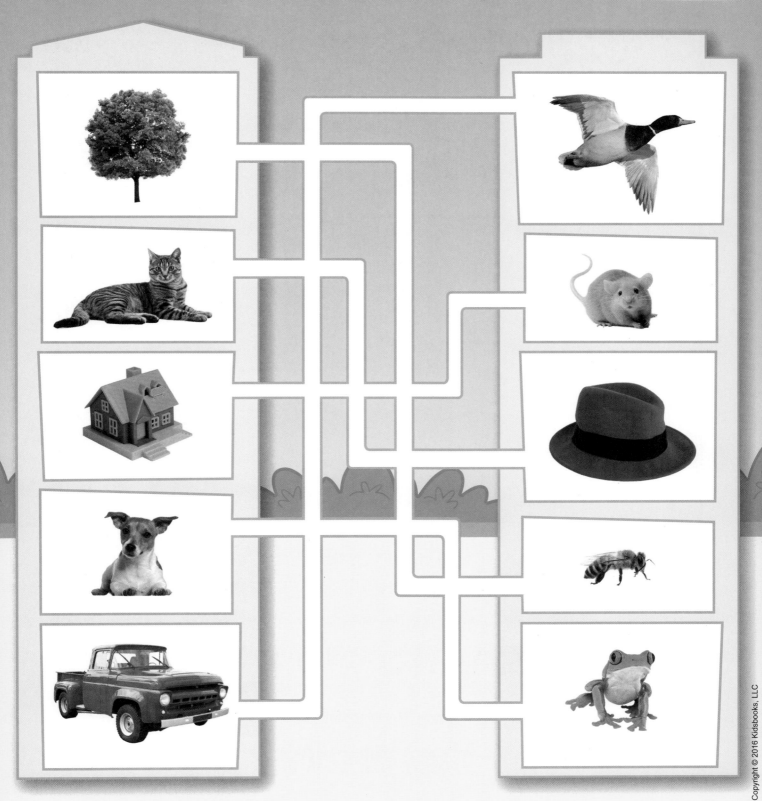

ANSWERS

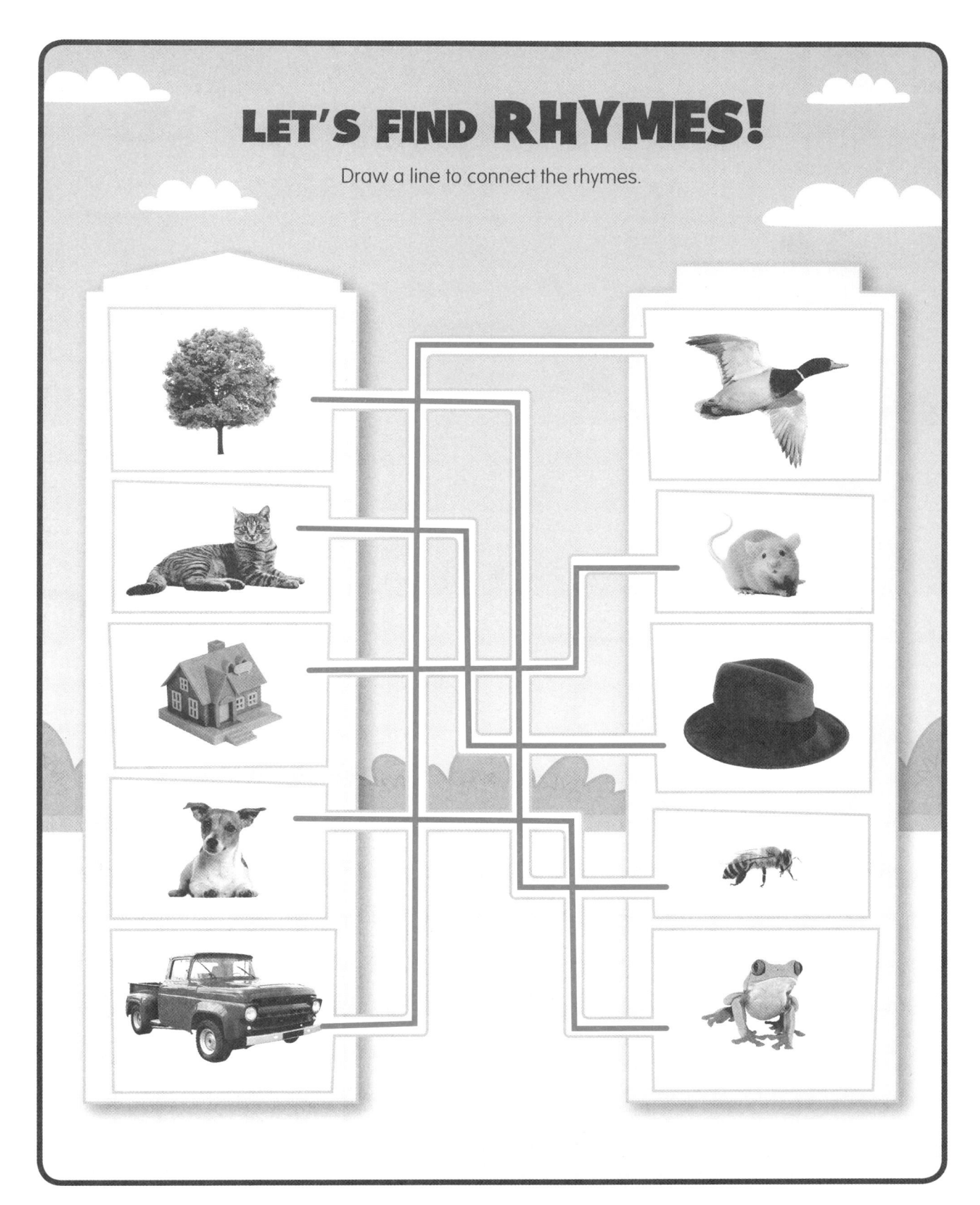

LET'S FIND RHYMES!

Draw a line to connect the rhymes.

MATCH THE LETTERS

Say the name of each picture out loud.
Circle the letter that begins its name.

a or **m**

o or **h**

b or **d**

t or **c**

d or **o**

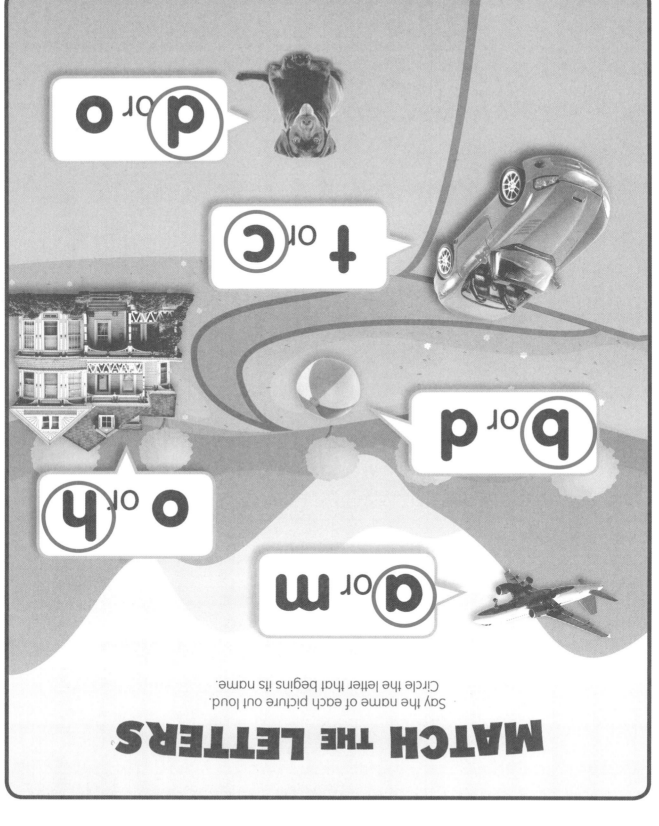

MATCH THE LETTERS

Say the name of each picture out loud.
Circle the letter that begins its name.

THE SAME SIZE

Draw a line to connect the frogs that are the same size.

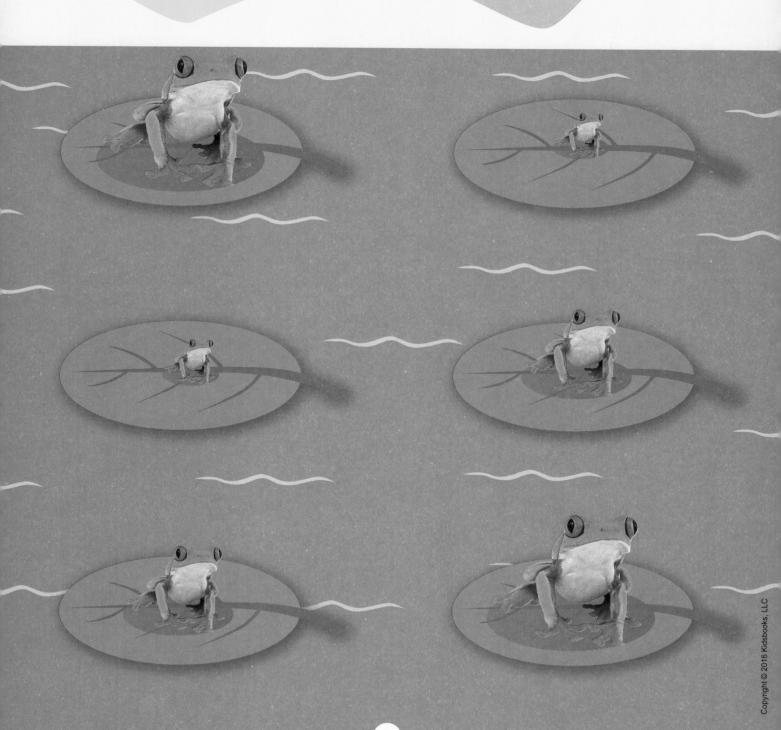

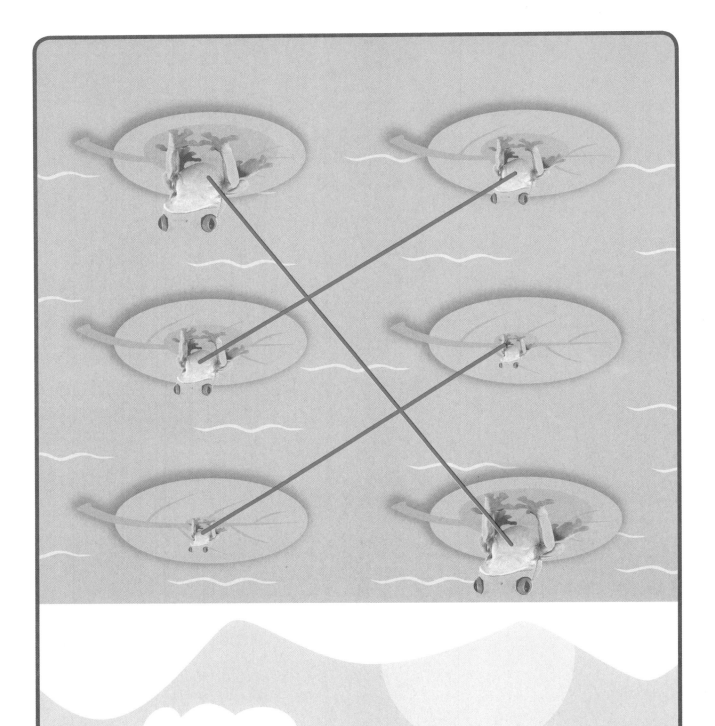

THE SAME SIZE

Draw a line to connect the frogs that are the same size.

WHICH HAS MORE?

Circle the group of pictures that has more.

ANSWERS

WHICH HAS MORE?

Circle the group of pictures that has more.

COUNTING FUN

Count the pictures in each row.
Circle the correct number.

9   2   4

7   4   5

3   6   2

8   5   3

ANSWERS

COUNTING FUN

Count the pictures in each row.
Circle the correct number.

9 (2) 4

(7) 4 5

3 (6) 2

8 5 (3)

TRACE THE MISSING NUMBERS

Trace the missing numbers to complete the numbers **1** to **10**. Then say each number out loud.

1   2   3

4   5   6

7   8   9   10

ANSWERS

TRACE THE MISSING NUMBERS

Trace the missing numbers to complete the numbers 1 to 10. Then say each number out loud.

1   2   3

4   5   6

7   8   9   10

MATCH THE PICTURE TO THE LETTER

Draw a line to match the picture to the letter it starts with.

R

S

L

P

ANSWERS

MATCH THE PICTURE TO THE LETTER

Draw a line to match the picture to the letter it starts with.

R

S

L

P

This or That?

cow **or** zebra

jaguar **or** rooster

farmer **or** astronaut

dinosaur **or** horse

73

ANSWERS

This or That?

Draw a circle around the animals or people found on a farm.

cow   **or**   zebra

jaguar   **or**   rooster

farmer   **or**   astronaut

dinosaur   **or**   horse

Search & Find®

Monsters at the Playground

Search & Find® the pictures of the things around the playground. Circle each thing as you find it.

| bucket | monster with balloon | monster dog | monster eating ice cream | radio |

ANSWERS

Search & Find®

Monsters at the Playground

Search & Find® the pictures of the things around the playground. Circle each thing as you find it.

bucket

monster with balloon

monster dog

monster eating ice cream

radio

LET'S LEARN SHAPES

Pizza is the yummiest triangle of all! Trace the triangle to make a pizza slice, then draw your favorite toppings!

 PIZZA TOPPINGS!

ANSWERS

LET'S LEARN SHAPES

Pizza is the yummiest triangle of all! Trace the triangle to make a pizza slice, then draw your favorite toppings!

PIZZA TOPPINGS!

PICK A PET

Look at the pictures and draw a circle around the animals that are popular pets.

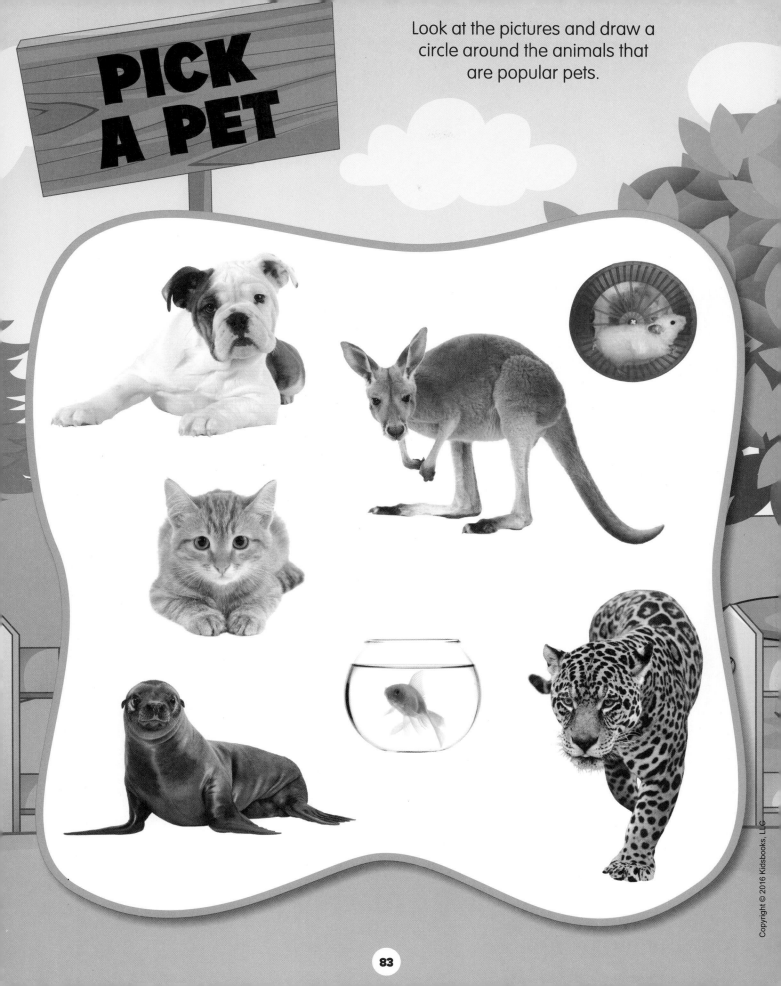

ANSWERS

PICK A PET

Look at the pictures and draw a circle around the animals that are popular pets.

MATCH THE PICTURES

Draw a line to connect the pictures that go together.

ANSWERS

MATCH THE PICTURES

Draw a line to connect the pictures that go together.

This or That?

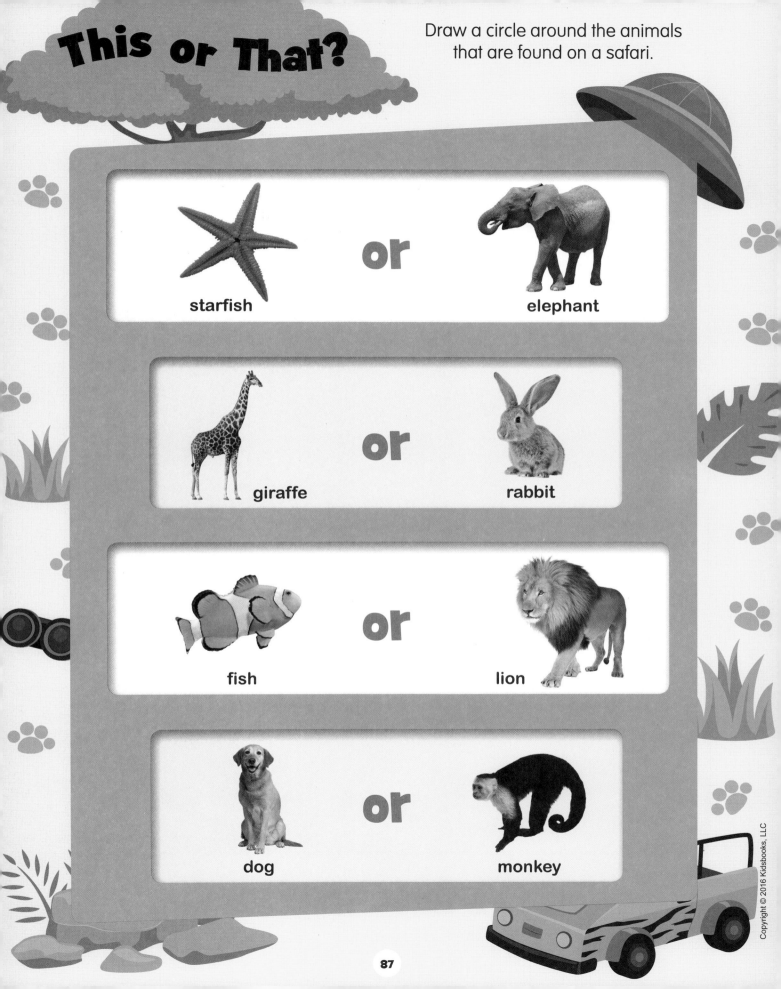

starfish **or** elephant

giraffe **or** rabbit

fish **or** lion

dog **or** monkey

ANSWERS

This or That?

Draw a circle around the animals that are found on a safari.

starfish **or** elephant

giraffe **or** rabbit

fish **or** lion

dog **or** monkey

SWEET OR SOUR?

Look at the pictures and circle the foods that taste sweet. Put an **X** over the foods that taste sour.

89

SWEET OR SOUR?

Look at the pictures and circle the foods that taste sweet. Put an X over the foods that taste sour.

JUMPING LITTLE MONKEYS

Count how many little monkeys are jumping and playing **on the bed!**
Circle the correct number.

6 3 8 10 2

ANSWERS

JUMPING LITTLE MONKEYS

Count how many little monkeys are jumping and playing **on the bed!** Circle the correct number.

(6)   3   8   10   2

SPOT THE DIFFERENCE

Draw an **X** over the cat that is not like the others.

ANSWERS

SPOT THE DIFFERENCE

Draw an **X** over the cat that is not like the others.

WHOSE TAIL IS THIS?

Draw a line to connect the tail to the animal it belongs to.

WHOSE TAIL IS THIS?

Draw a line to connect the tail to the animal it belongs to.

FIREFIGHTER MATCH

Circle the things a firefighter needs to save the day.

ANSWERS

FIREFIGHTER MATCH

Circle the things a firefighter needs to save the day.

OPPOSITES

Draw a line from the top row to the bottom row to match the two things that are opposites.

full   dirty t-shirt   big dog

clean t-shirt   small dog   empty

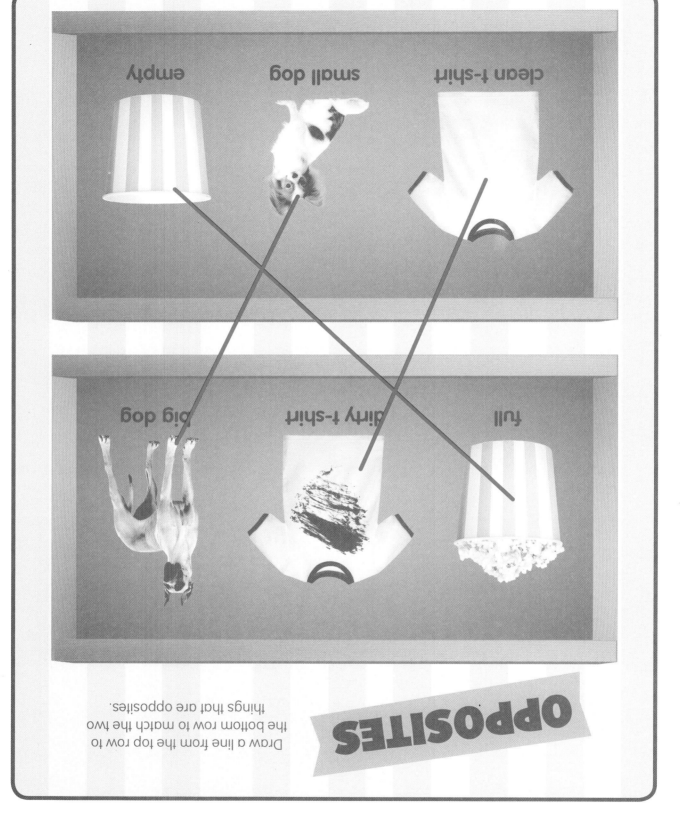

empty

small dog

clean t-shirt

big dog

dirty t-shirt

full

OPPOSITES

Draw a line from the top row to the bottom row to match the two things that are opposites.

ANSWERS

MATCH THE SOUND

Match the creature with the sound it makes.
Then say each sound out loud!

roar

meow

neigh

ooh ha ha

cheep

ANSWERS

HALLOWEEN CANDY

Circle the **4** treats you might get on Halloween.
Watch out for tricks!

ANSWERS

HALLOWEEN CANDY

Circle the **4** treats you might get on Halloween.
Watch out for tricks!

SPOT THE DIFFERENCE

Draw an **X** over the airplane that is not like the others.

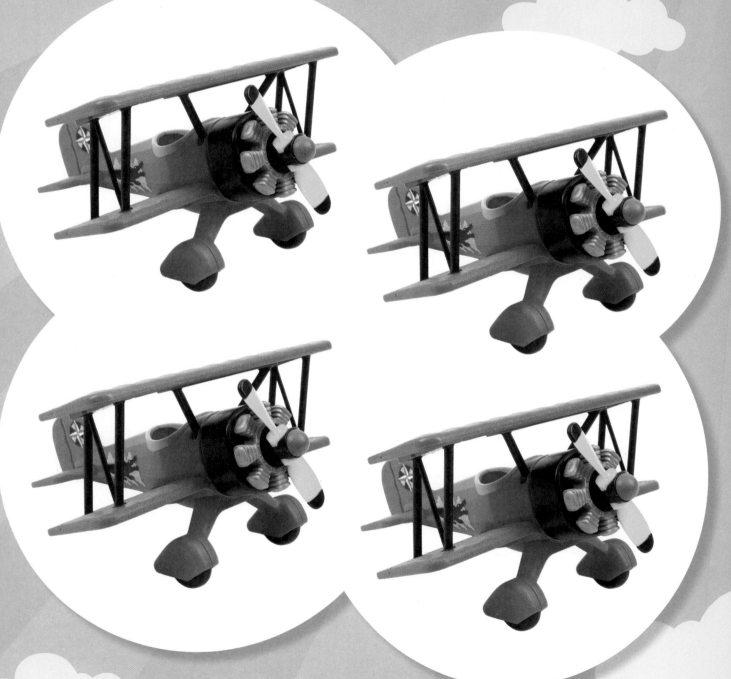

ANSWERS

SPOT THE DIFFERENCE

Draw an **X** over the airplane that is not like the others.

CIRCLE THE LETTERS

Say the name of each animal.
Circle the letter that begins each name.

c or t

n or m

h or f

d or b

ANSWERS

SET THE TABLE

Circle the food that you can eat with the utensils that are set below at each plate.

ANSWERS

ANSWERS

SET THE TABLE

Circle the food that you can eat with the utensils that are set below at each plate.

LET'S FIND SEA ANIMALS

Look at the scene. Draw a circle around the **8** sea creatures.

ANSWERS

LET'S FIND SEA ANIMALS

Look at the scene. Draw a circle around the **8** sea creatures.

PLAY WITH PATTERNS

There are shapes everywhere!
Each row of shapes makes a pattern.
Finish each pattern by drawing the
shape that comes next.

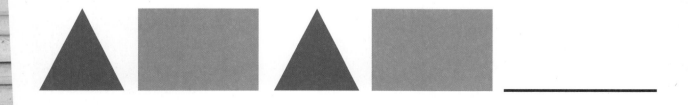

ANSWERS

PLAY WITH PATTERNS

There are shapes everywhere! Each row of shapes makes a pattern. Finish each pattern by drawing the shape that comes next.

HOW TO DRAW A FLOWER

Copy the pictures below to draw a flower in the flowerpot.

ANSWERS

HOW TO DRAW A FLOWER

Copy the pictures below to draw a flower in the flowerpot.

INSIDE, OUTSIDE

Circle the pictures that show a cat inside something.

ANSWERS

INSIDE, OUTSIDE

Circle the pictures that show a cat inside something.

HOT DOG STAND

Do you love to eat a hot dog at a baseball game in the summer? Circle toppings you might put on a hot dog!

ANSWERS

HOT DOG STAND

HOT DOG STAND

Do you love to eat a hot dog at a baseball game in the summer? Circle toppings you might put on a hot dog!

This or That?

Draw a circle around the things you'll find at a day care.

 **friends**

or

 **snake**

 **teacher**

or

 **monkey**

 **hippopotamus**

or

 crayons

 **blocks**

or

 **lifesaver**

ANSWERS

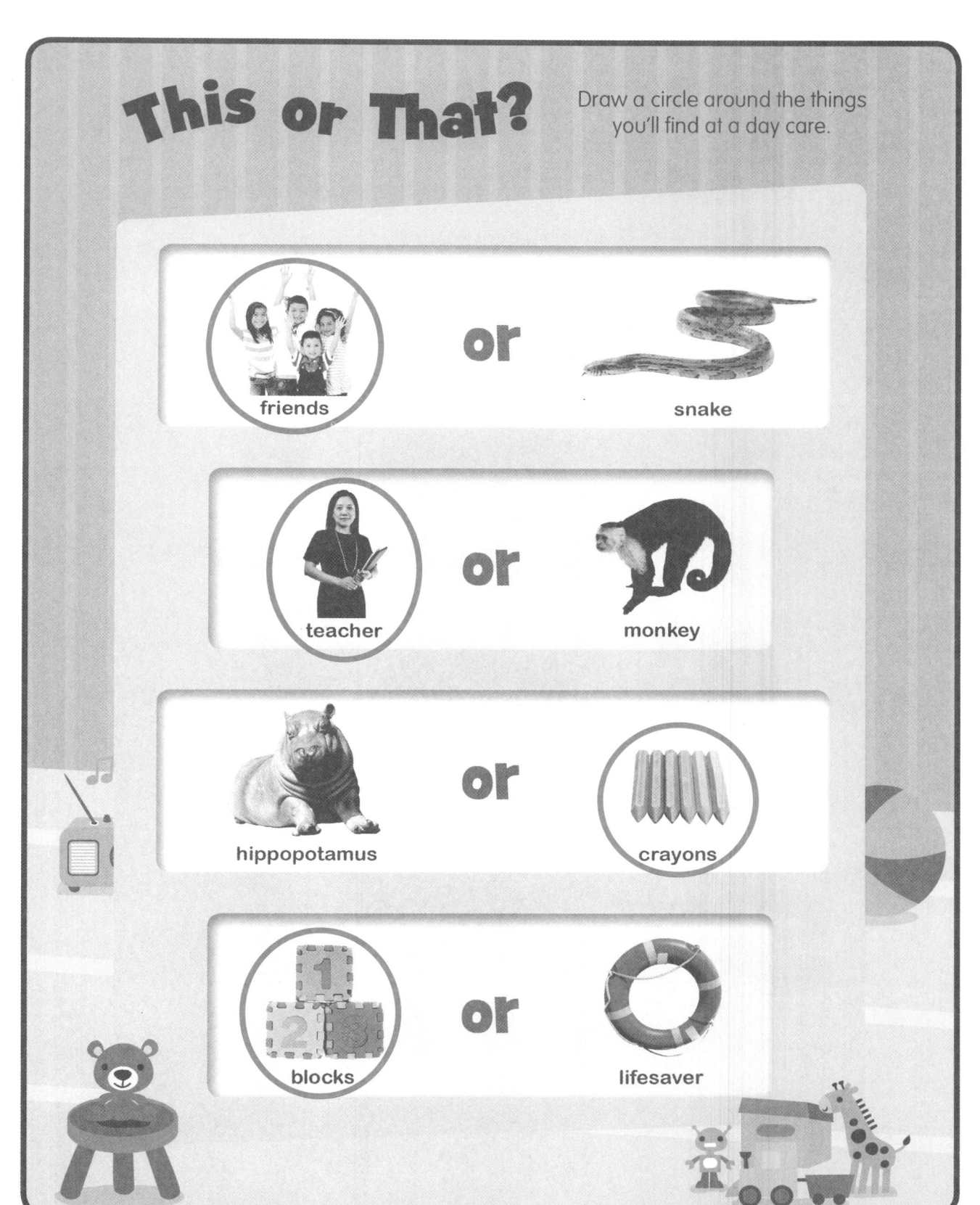

This or That?

Draw a circle around the things you'll find at a day care.

friends **or** snake

teacher **or** monkey

hippopotamus **or** crayons

blocks **or** lifesaver

WHICH IS SHORTER?

Circle the picture in each group that shows something that's shorter.

ANSWERS

WHICH IS SHORTER?

Circle the picture in each group that shows something that's shorter.

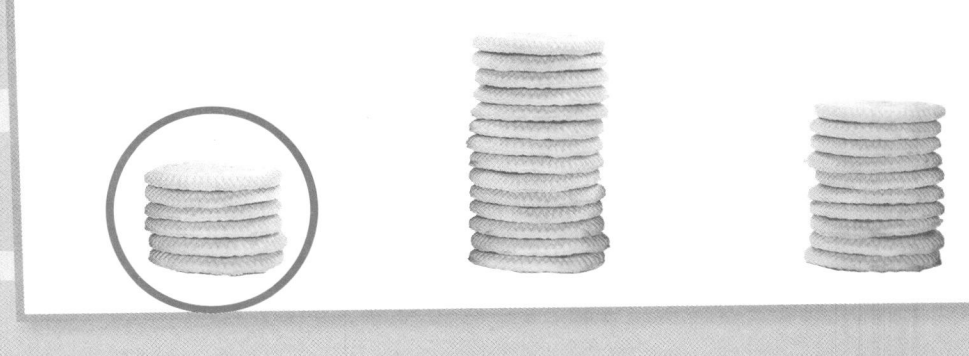

Which has More?

Circle the basket that has more fruit in it.

ANSWERS

Which has More?

Circle the basket that has more fruit in it.

COLORFUL BUTTERFLIES

Butterflies come in many colors! Circle the butterflies that are red. Put an **X** over the butterflies that are yellow. Draw a square around the butterflies that are blue.

ANSWERS

COLORFUL BUTTERFLIES

Butterflies come in many colors! Circle the butterflies that are red. Put an **X** over the butterflies that are yellow. Draw a square around the butterflies that are blue.

SPOT THE DIFFERENCE

Circle the parrot that is not like the others.

Circle the parrot that is not like the others.

ANSWERS

OUTER SPACE

Circle *the* biggest planet!

Mercury

Venus

Mars

Earth

Jupiter

Uranus

Saturn

How many planets are in the picture?

_____

Neptune

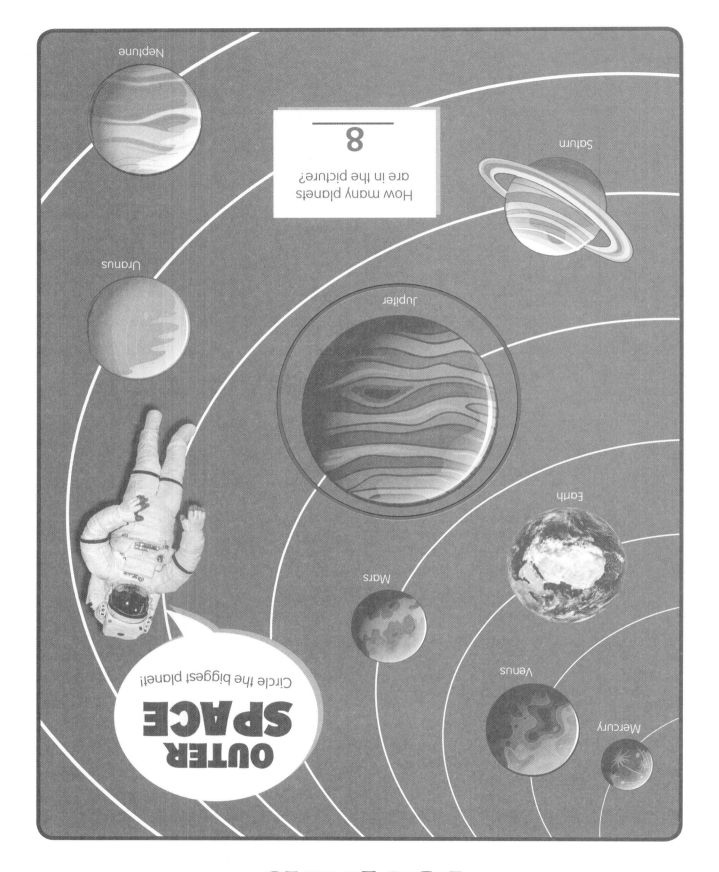

OUTER SPACE

Circle the biggest planet!

Mercury

Venus

Earth

Mars

Jupiter

Saturn

Uranus

Neptune

How many planets
are in the picture?

8

READY, SET, GO!

Trace the line of each animal to help them get to the finish line.

Trace the line of each animal to help them get to the finish line.

READY, SET, GO!

WHICH DOESN'T BELONG?

Look at the pictures and make an **X** over the picture that doesn't belong in the group.

143

ANSWERS

WHICH DOESN'T BELONG?

Look at the pictures and make an **X** over the picture that doesn't belong in the group.

FIND TWO THAT ARE THE SAME

Circle two pictures that are exactly the same.

ANSWERS

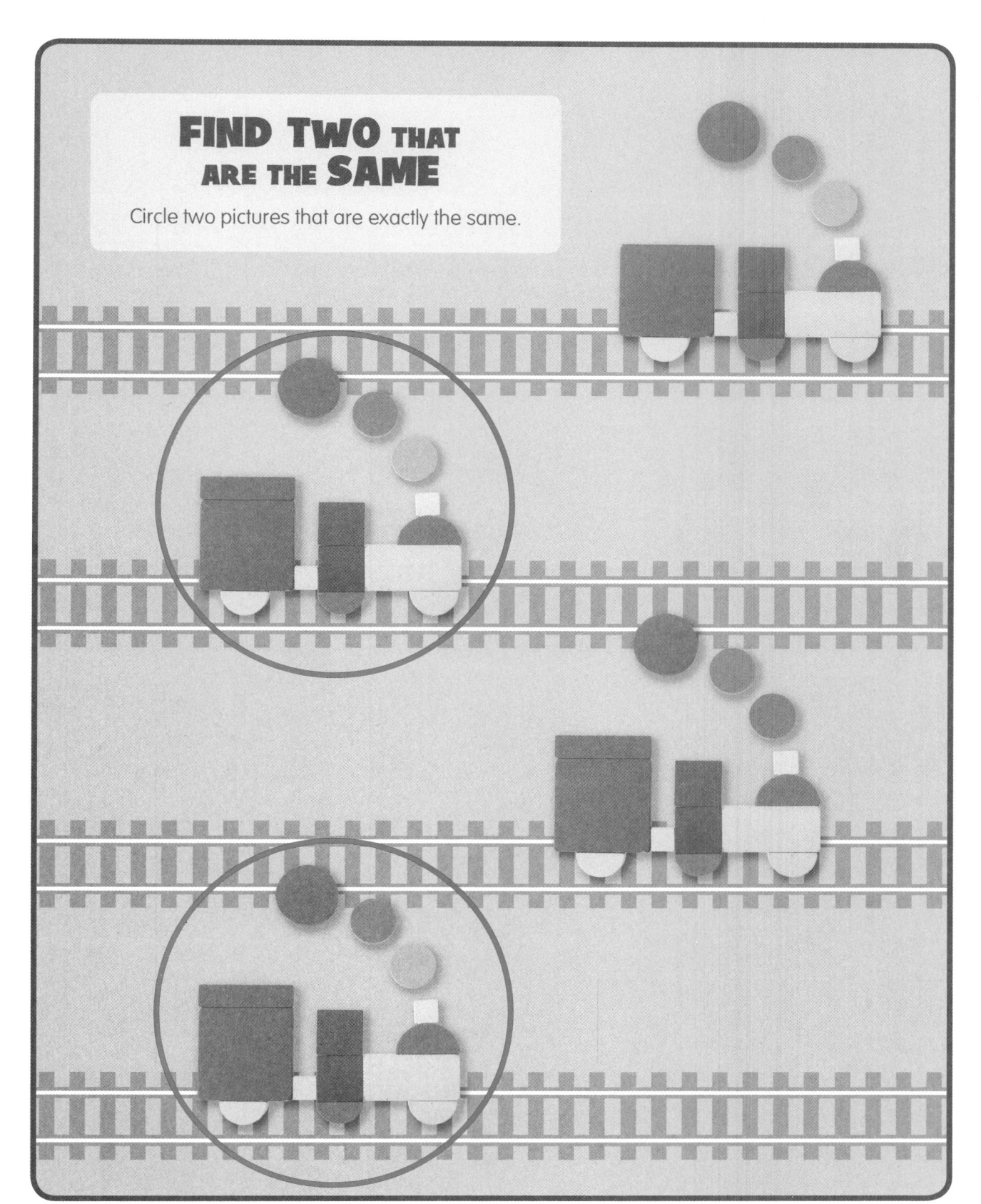

FIND TWO THAT ARE THE SAME

Circle two pictures that are exactly the same.

HOW MANY STARS?

Draw **3** stars in this pretty night sky. Then count how many stars there are and circle the correct number.

How many stars?

7   12   9

3   5   4

HOW MANY STARS?

Draw **3** stars in this pretty night sky. Then count how many stars there are and circle the correct number.

How many stars?

7 9 12 5 3

4 5 3

EMPTY OR FULL?

Circle the picture in each group that shows something that is full.
Put an **X** over the picture that shows something that's empty.

149

ANSWERS

EMPTY OR FULL?

Circle the picture in each group that shows something that is full.
Put an X over the picture that shows something that's empty.

WHICH COMES FIRST?

Circle the picture in each row that comes first.

ANSWERS

WHICH COMES FIRST?

Circle the picture in each row that comes first.

SNACK TIME

Everybody gets hungry during the day. Circle the snacks you might find in a lunch box.

ANSWERS

SNACK TIME

Everybody gets hungry during the day. Circle the snacks you might find in a lunch box.

Making Words

Trace each word. Then write each
word in the blank space below.

bird   cat   dog

bird   cat   dog

Draw here

Making Words

Trace each word. Then write each
word in the blank space below.

bird   cat   dog

bird   cat   dog

bird   cat   dog

bird   cat   dog

Draw here

WHICH DOESN'T BELONG?

Look at the picture of the night sky and circle the **3** things that don't belong.

WHICH DOESN'T BELONG?

Look at the picture of the night sky and circle the **3** things that don't belong.

ANSWERS

LET'S MATCH

Everybody has different thumb prints. Match the body part to what its print would look like.

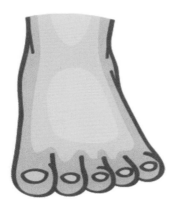

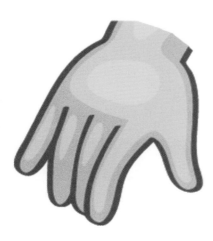

ANSWERS

LET'S MATCH

Everybody has different thumb prints. Match the body part to what its print would look like.

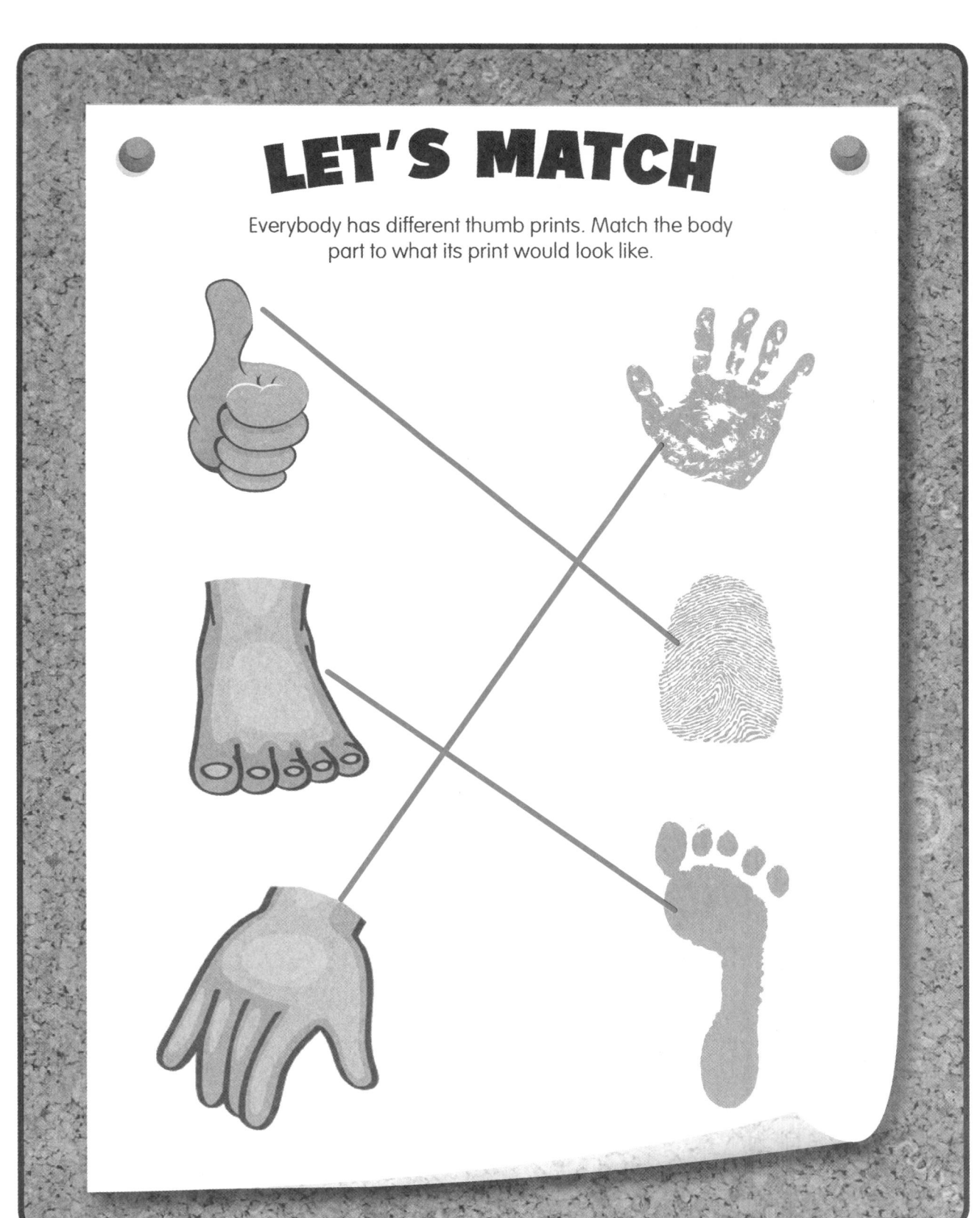

SPOT THE DIFFERENCE

There are **5** differences between these pictures. Find the differences and circle them.

ANSWERS

SPOT THE DIFFERENCE

There are **5** differences between these pictures. Find the differences and circle them.

WACKY CRITTERS

Some things are make believe. Circle the creatures that are **not** real.

WACKY CRITTERS

Some things are make
believe. Circle the creatures
that are **not** real.

ANSWERS

FINISH THE PICTURE

There's a whole world of animals that live under the sea!
Use markers or crayons to finish the under-the-sea scene.

ANSWERS

LET'S GO TO THE MOVIES

Follow the trail of tickets to get to the movie!
Don't step on the candy or popcorn!
You may not move diagonally.

Start

Finish

ANSWERS

LET'S GO TO THE MOVIES

Follow the trail of tickets to get to the movie!
Don't step on the candy or popcorn!
You may not move diagonally.

Start

Finish

TRACE THE LINES

It's time to put away the toys!
Draw a line from the toys on
the floor to the toy box.

ANSWERS

TRACE THE LINES

It's time to put away the toys!
Draw a line from the toys on
the floor to the toy box.

Let's plant a Garden!

Circle the things you would need to plant a garden.

ANSWERS

Let's plant a Garden!

Circle the things you would need to plant a garden.

LET'S DRAW CIRCLES

Trace the circles in the picture. Then count how many circles you traced.

Circles: _____

ANSWERS

LET'S
DRAW
CIRCLES

Trace the circles in the picture.
Then count how many
circles you traced.

Circles: __5__

FISHING BOWL FUN!

How many fish can you find in each color?
Write the number you find in the boxes below.

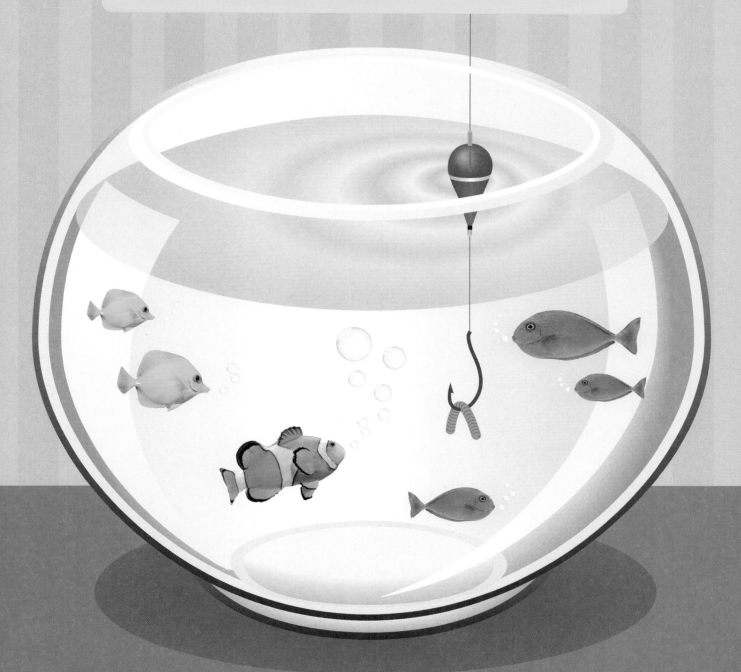

ORANGE

BLUE

PINK

ANSWERS

FISHING BOWL FUN!

How many fish can you find in each color?
Write the number you find in the boxes below.

ORANGE	BLUE	PINK
1	3	2

DUCK, DUCK, GOOSE!

Let's play this fun playground game on paper! Draw a line connecting duck to duck to goose, from start to finish.

Start

Finish

ANSWERS

DUCK, DUCK, GOOSE!

Let's play this fun playground game on paper! Draw a line connecting duck to duck to goose, from start to finish.

Start

Finish

LET'S MATCH COLORS TO THE RAINBOW

Draw a line from each fruit to the same color on the rainbow.

ANSWERS

LET'S MATCH COLORS TO THE RAINBOW

Draw a line from each fruit to the same color on the rainbow.

What's Your Name?

Circle the first letter of your name.
Then write your name in the lines below.

A B C D E

F G H I J

K L M N O P

Q R S T U

V W X Y Z

_____

- - - - - - - - - - - - - - -

_____

What's Your Name?

Circle the first letter of your name.
Then write your name in the lines below.

A	B	C	D	(E)
F	G	H	I	J
K	L	M	N	O	P
Q	R	S	T	U
V	W	X	Y	Z

EMILY

WHICH ANIMALS LAY EGGS?

Welcome to the baby animal petting zoo! Do you know which baby hatched from an egg? Circle the **4** animals that lay eggs.

ANSWERS

WHICH ANIMALS LAY EGGS?

Welcome to the baby animal petting zoo! Do you know which baby hatched from an egg? Circle the **4** animals that lay eggs.

FOLLOW THE MAZE

Help the mermaid through the maze to the treasure chest. The correct path is made up of only starfish. You may not move diagonally.

Start →

↓
Finish

Finish

Start

FOLLOW THE MAZE

Help the mermaid through the maze to the treasure chest. The correct path is made up of only starfish. You may not move diagonally.

ABOVE OR BELOW

Circle the picture that shows the animal above or on top of something.

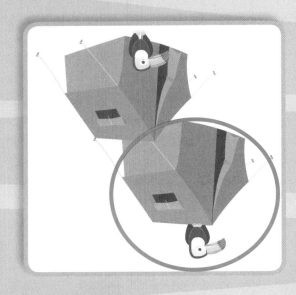

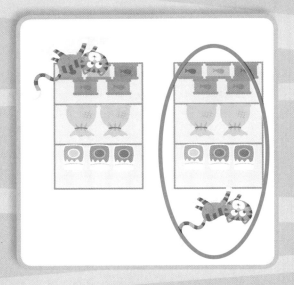

Circle the picture that shows the animal above or on top of something.

ABOVE OR BELOW

FINISH THE PATTERN

Help! This eel is missing some of his spots! His spots make a pattern. Fill in the missing shapes to finish the pattern.

ANSWERS

FINISH THE PATTERN

Help! This eel is missing some of his spots! His spots make a pattern. Fill in the missing shapes to finish the pattern.

HEAVY OR LIGHT?

Look at each picture. Circle the things that are heavy. Put an **X** over the things that are light.

HEAVY OR LIGHT?

Look at each picture. Circle the things that are heavy. Put an X over the things that are light.

WHO AM I?

Read the clues given for each animal. Draw a circle around the animal that best fits the description.

1   I am an animal who likes to chew logs. I make my bed in the river.

Who am I?

2   I am an animal that is mostly seen at night. I like to greet the moon by saying, "Hooo! Hooo! Hooo!"

Who am I?

3   You might find me on a farm. I'm pink and I say, "Oink, oink!"

Who am I?

ANSWERS

WHO AM I?

Read the clues given for each animal. Draw a circle around the animal that best fits the description.

1 I am an animal who likes to chew logs. I make my bed in the river.

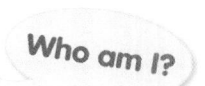 Who am I?

2 I am an animal that is mostly seen at night. I like to greet the moon by saying, "Hooo! Hooo! Hooo!"

 Who am I?

3 You might find me on a farm. I'm pink and I say, "Oink, oink!"

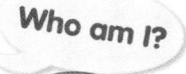 Who am I?

LET'S SORT SOCKS!

Help sort the laundry by drawing a line to connect the socks that go together.

ANSWERS

LET'S SORT SOCKS!

Help sort the laundry by drawing a line to connect the socks that go together.

BUSY BEE

Connect the dots from **1** to **10** to finish the picture of the bee.

ANSWERS

BUSY BEE

Connect the dots from **1** to **10** to finish the picture of the bee.

SPOT THE DIFFERENCE

Draw an **X** over the puppy that is not like the others.

ANSWERS

SPOT THE DIFFERENCE

Draw an **X** over the puppy that is not like the others.

WHICH DOESN'T BELONG?

Look at the apples and make an **X** over the apple that doesn't match the others.

WHICH DOESN'T BELONG?

Look at the apples and make an X over the apple that doesn't match the others.

LET'S COLOR

Use a marker or crayons to color in each shape.

ANSWERS

LET'S COLOR

Use a marker or crayons to color in each shape.

MATCH THE HAT

Draw a line to match the hat to
the thing that goes with it.

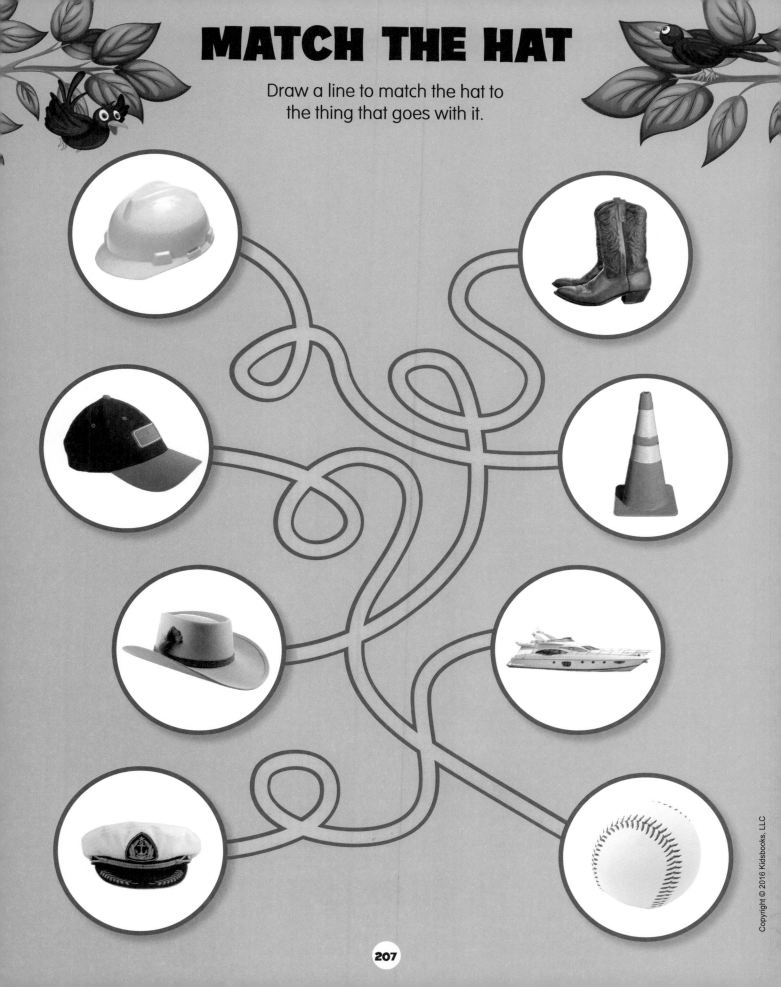

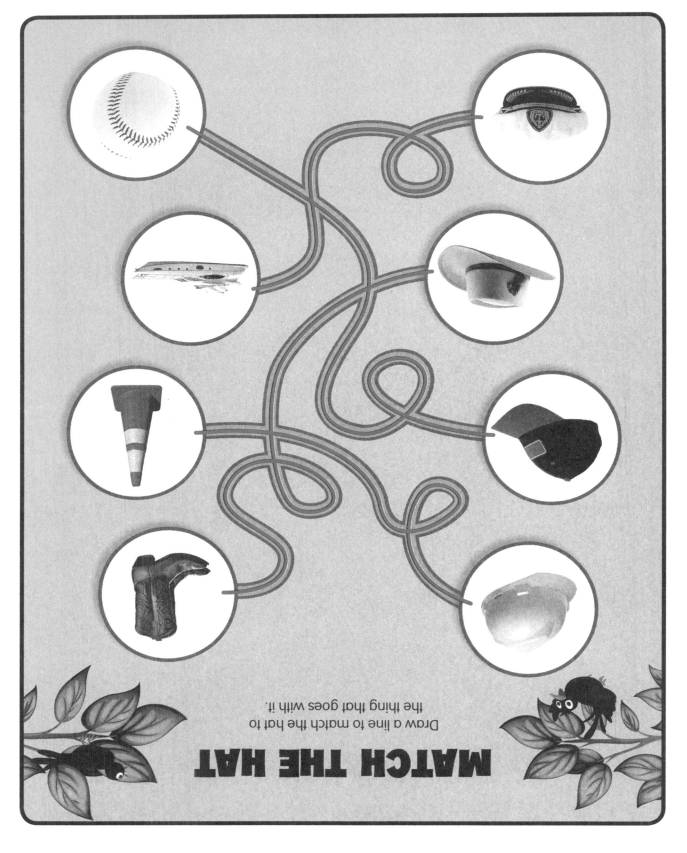

MATCH THE HAT

Draw a line to match the hat to the thing that goes with it.

COUNT THE BIRDS

There are many different kinds of birds.
Count the birds in this picture and
circle the correct number.

1 2 3 4 5 6 7 8 9 10

209

ANSWERS

COUNT THE BIRDS

There are many different kinds of birds. Count the birds in this picture and circle the correct number.

1 2 3 4 5 6 7 8 ⑨ 10

MATCH THE PICTURES

Draw a line to connect the pictures that go together.

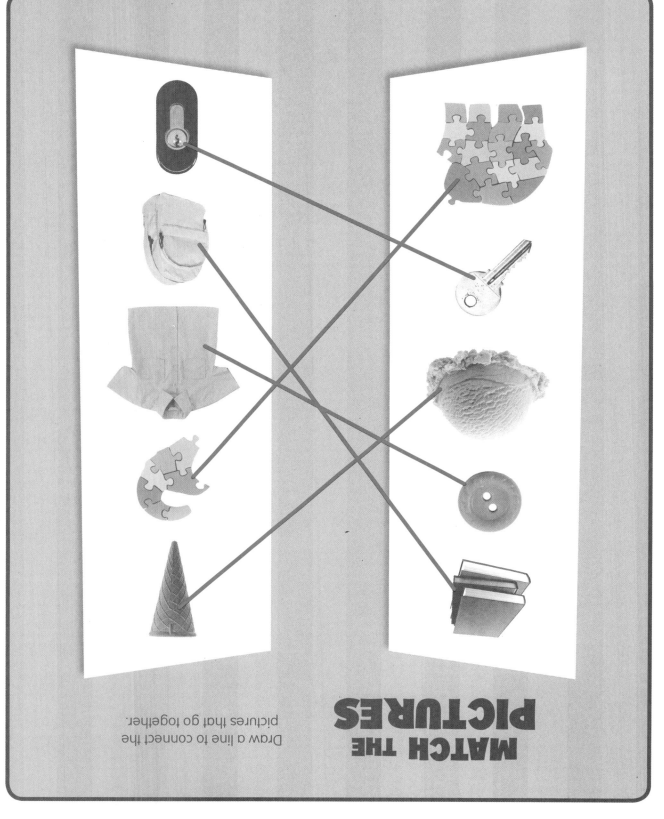

MATCH THE PICTURES

Draw a line to connect the pictures that go together.

This or That?

Draw a circle around the things you might find **inside** your house.

 **utensils** **or**  **elephant**

 **clown** **or**  **bananas**

 **hot air balloon** **or**  **chair**

 **laptop** **or**  **airplane**

ANSWERS

This or That?

Draw a circle around the things you might find **inside** your house.

utensils _or_ elephant

clown _or_ bananas

hot air balloon _or_ chair

laptop _or_ airplane

WHO LIVES IN THE DARK?

Some animals only come out at night!
These are called nocturnal animals.
Circle the nocturnal animals.

bat **or** squirrel

skunk **or** bird

goose **or** opossum

owl **or** horse

ANSWERS

WHO LIVES IN THE DARK?

Some animals only come out at night!
These are called nocturnal animals.
Circle the nocturnal animals.

bat

or

squirrel

bird

or

skunk

goose

or

opossum

owl

or

horse

DOGS AND CATS

Draw a line to connect the paw prints that belong to the cat and the paw prints that belong to the dog.

Draw a line to connect the paw prints
that belong to the cat and the paw
prints that belong to the dog.

DOGS AND CATS

ANSWERS

Let's Bake a Cake!

Circle the things you would need to bake a cake.

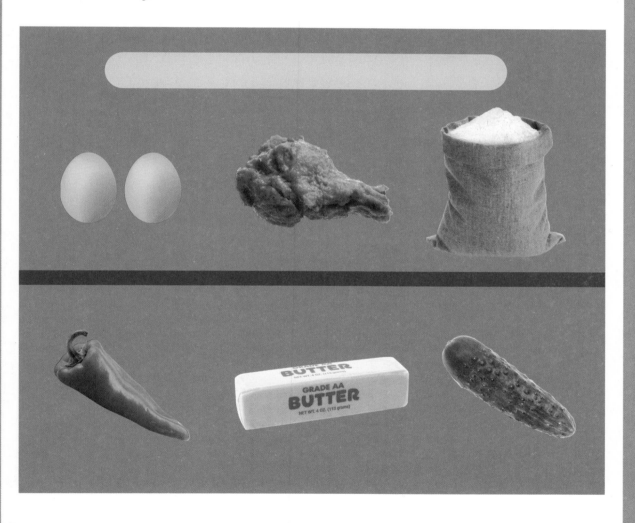

BUTTER

GRADE AA
BUTTER
NET WT. 4 OZ. (110 grams)

Let's Bake a Cake!

Circle the things you would need to bake a cake.

TIME FOR BREAKFAST

Draw a line to connect the pictures that go together.

ANSWERS

TIME FOR BREAKFAST

Draw a line to connect the pictures that go together.

LET'S FIND THE COLORS

Draw a line to connect the pictures to the square with the same color. Each square shows how many things there are of that color.

1   2   3

LET'S FIND THE COLORS

Draw a line to connect the pictures to the
square with the same color. Each square
shows how many things there are of that color.

1 2 3

Let's Get Ready for School!

Circle the pictures of the things you might find in a classroom.

ANSWERS

Let's Get Ready for School!

Circle the pictures of the things you might find in a classroom.

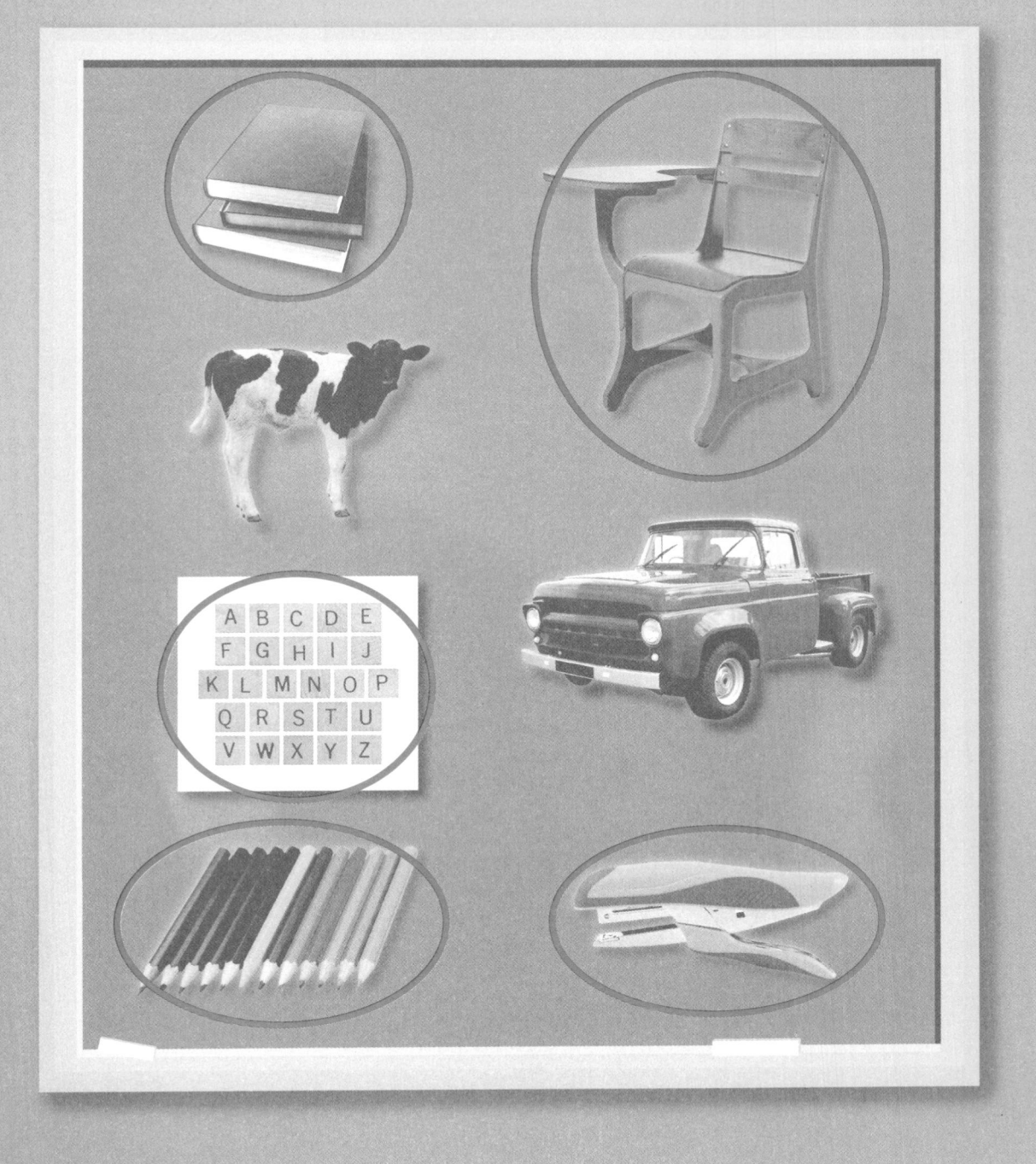

WHICH IS THE HEALTHIEST CHOICE?

Circle which food in each group is the healthiest.

ANSWERS

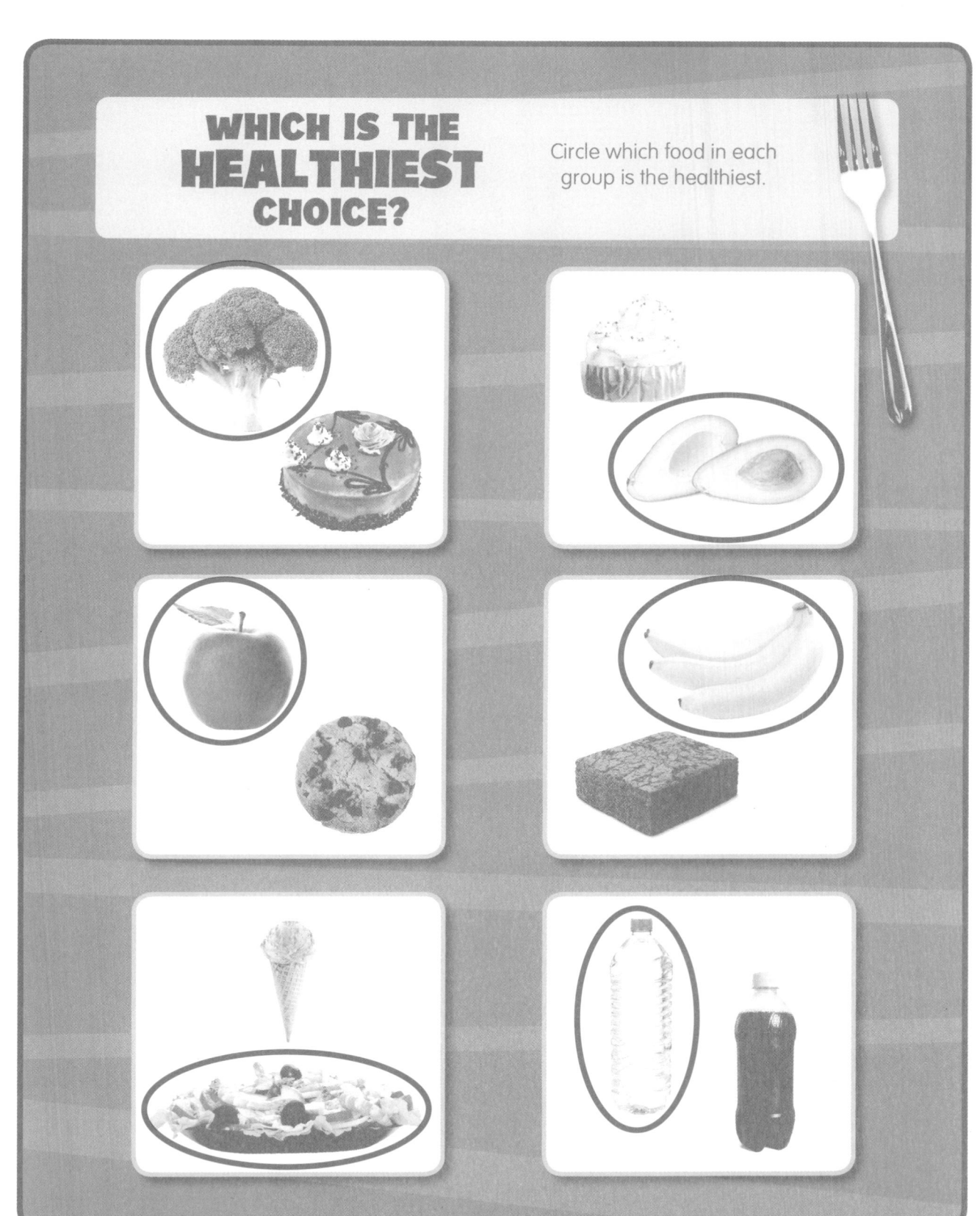

WHICH IS THE HEALTHIEST CHOICE?

Circle which food in each group is the healthiest.

WHO WILL WIN THE RACE?

Circle the picture of the animal that moves fastest.

ANSWERS

FIND TWO THAT ARE THE SAME

Only one of the cowboys below is the same as the cowboy to the left. Draw a circle around the cowboy that is the same.

WANTED

WILD WEST

ANSWERS

WANTED

FIND TWO THAT ARE THE SAME

Only one of the cowboys below is the same as the cowboy to the left. Draw a circle around the cowboy that is the same.

WILD WEST

BUILD A SNOWMAN

Draw the missing pieces where they go on the snowman.

ANSWERS

BUILD A SNOWMAN

Draw the missing pieces where they go on the snowman.

WHICH IS AN INSECT?

Did you know that bugs are not animals? They're insects! Draw a circle around the **4** bugs.

ANSWERS

WHICH IS AN INSECT?

Did you know that bugs are not animals? They're insects! Draw a circle around the **4** bugs.

Beep! Beep!

The monster got a cool new car for his birthday! Help him color it so he can go for a ride!

ANSWERS

CLEAN YOUR ROOM

This bedroom is messy! Can you find and circle the missing teddy bear?

ANSWERS

CLEAN YOUR ROOM

This bedroom is messy! Can you find and circle the missing teddy bear?

WHICH ONE WHISTLES?

Circle the animal that whistles a song.

ANSWERS

WHICH ONE WHISTLES?

Circle the animal that whistles a song.

Find the ABCs

Help the puppy find and circle A, B, C.
Then trace them below.

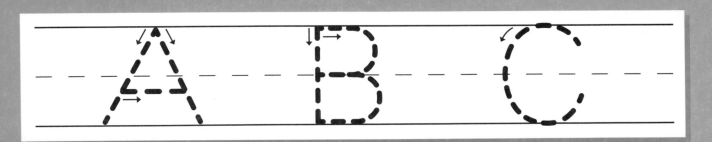

ANSWERS

Find the ABCs

Help the puppy find and circle A, B, C.
Then trace them below.

LET'S DRAW SQUARES

Trace the squares in the picture. Then count how many squares you traced.

Squares: _____

ANSWERS

Trace the squares in the picture. Then count how many squares you traced.

Squares: 5

Making Animals with Shapes

Draw a cat's face!

1. Trace a large circle.

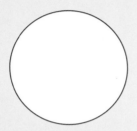

2. Trace two small triangles for ears.

3. Draw whiskers, eyes, and a mouth on your cat's face.

ANSWERS

Making Animals with Shapes

Draw a cat's face!

1. Trace a large circle.

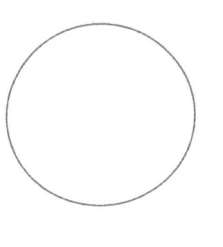

2. Trace two small triangles for ears.

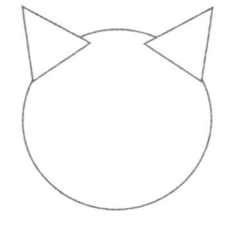

3. Draw whiskers, eyes, and a mouth on your cat's face.

RIGHT or LEFT?

Circle the picture that shows the monster to the right of something.

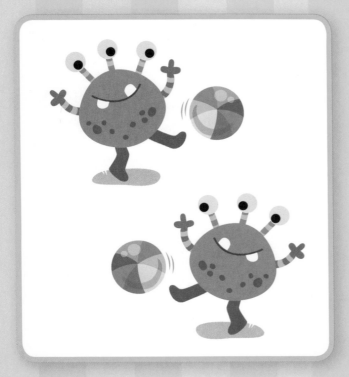

ANSWERS

RIGHT or LEFT?

Circle the picture that shows the monster to the right of something.

WHICH DOESN'T BELONG?

Look at each group of pictures.
Circle the picture that doesn't belong.

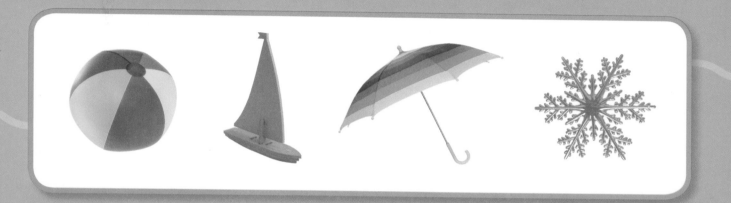

ANSWERS

WHICH DOESN'T BELONG?

Look at each group of pictures. Circle the picture that doesn't belong.

LET'S COLOR

Color the tree in each season: winter, spring, summer, and fall!

WINTER

SPRING

SUMMER

FALL

ANSWERS

LET'S COLOR

Color the tree in each season: winter, spring, summer, and fall!

WINTER

SPRING

SUMMER

FALL

Swinging JUNGLE

Draw a line through the maze of vines to swing from one tree to another!

Start

Finish

Swinging JUNGLE

Draw a line through the maze of vines to swing from one tree to another!

Start

Finish